NATURE'S PRESCRIPTION FOR OPTIMUM HEALTH

NUTRiBULLET**Rx**

CONTENTS

THE
NUTRiBULLET Rx

THE NEXT LEVEL OF EXTRACTION ®

AT THE TIME OF THIS BOOK'S PRINTING, over 10 million individuals will have joined the NutriBullet Revolution! Whether you've previously owned a NutriBullet, or are just starting your journey with our line of products, your purchase of the NutriBullet Rx proves your commitment to health and wellness.

EATING A DIET RICH IN FRUITS AND VEGETABLES HAS PROVEN TO BE ONE OF THE BEST STEPS TO TAKE ON THE PATH TO LONGEVITY. A recent study conducted by the Universtity College of London found a 42% decrease in mortality rates among individuals who ate 7 or more servings of fresh fruits and vegetables a day compared with those who ate less than one daily serving!

While those conclusions are impressive, consuming that much produce is not always easy. Fruits and vegetables generally require lots of preparation and lots of chewing to make it to your digestive system. Many complain about their taste, and many others have digestive disorders that can be agitated when taxed with the breakdown of high-fiber foods. This is where the **NutriBullet Rx** comes in.

With its 1700 horsepower motor, 7-minute heating cycle, and large vessel sizes, the **NutriBullet Rx** embodies the next progression in eating for longevity. This newest addition to the NutriBullet family allows you to make the NutriBlasts you know and love with more power than ever before, plus all-new **SouperBlasts**—pureed vegetable-based soups mixed and heated right in the machine! The power, speed, size, and heating capabilities of the **NutriBullet Rx** make it easier than ever to maximize your intake of vegetables, fruits, nuts, seeds, and other superfoods!

THE NUTRIBLAST RX: THE BEST OF ITS KIND

The **NutriBullet Rx** outperforms any other machine of its kind when it comes to breaking down plant foods, making the **NutriBlast Rx**—the delicious vegetable and fruit-based drink mixed inside the machine—one of the most powerfully nutritious meals available! Extracting a **NutriBlast Rx** in your Bullet allows you to quickly prepare and take in a full spectrum of veggies, fruits, and other superfoods in one convenient, smooth, and delicious beverage!

INTRODUCING THE SOUPERBLAST

In addition to its incredible extraction powers, the **NutriBullet Rx** features a 7-Minute Heating Cycle that turns your favorite vegetables, fruits, nuts, seeds, and spices into delicious, piping hot **SouperBlasts**. **SouperBlasts** have the taste and texture of puréed soups, but contain the power of extracted nutrition within. Simply add your ingredients to the vent–topped **SouperBlast** Pitcher and press the G-Button to activate the Heating Cycle. In seven minutes, you will have a multi-serving batch of a warm and delicious superfood **SouperBlast**.

VITALITY

WHILE NUTRITION IS A COMPLEX FIELD OF STUDY, nature gives us much of the information we need to choose our produce according to our personal health requirements. The easiest way to identify the nutrition locked within a given food is by looking at its color.

Our minds and bodies naturally associate different colored foods with different health needs: Have you ever found yourself craving oranges, orange juice, or carrots when you feel a cold coming on? This is due in part to the fact that they contain immune-boosting vitamin C and carotenoids—nutrients that work to fight off infection and illness in the body. Is your system calling for green juices and salads after a night of overindulging? On some level, you know that green foods contain the cleansing and detoxifying nutrients your body needs to regain its balance.

The **NutriBullet Rx** aims to empower you with an understanding of the nutritional clues provided by nature's color spectrum. When you can recognize the vitamins and minerals associated with specific fruit and vegetable coloration, as well as the bodily systems and functions those nutrients support, you can make informed decisions on how to eat to address your specific health needs.

In the following section, you will find the **NutriBullet Rx Nature's Prescription Quiz.** This quiz asks an extensive array of health-oriented questions to help you determine the best colors of foods for your system.

NOTE: While the physical color of recommended foods generally matches their color category, there are a few foods we have included in each category that match the health benefits of the others, but differ in color.

For example, avocado is labeled as a "Blue Brain Boosting" food despite its green color because it contains an exceptional amount of healthy fats that have been shown to support healthy brain function.

IN GENERAL, FOODS CAN BE CATEGORIZED AS FOLLOWS:

RED
ANTI-AGING

ORANGE
IMMUNE-BOOSTING

YELLOW
INFLAMMATION-REGULATING

GREEN
DETOXIFYING

BLUE
BRAIN-BOOSTING

For a full list of the categories, their associated benefits, recommended foods, and delicious recipes, consult our color section on **page 35.**

Take our **NutriBullet Rx** Color Quiz and find out what colors you should include in your **NutriBlast Rx's** and **SouperBlasts** to suit your specific health needs!

NATURE'S PRESCRIPTION QUIZ NUTRiBULLET Rx

01

Circle the points you score for each of your answers.

* DON'T WANT TO DO THE MATH?
Take the digital quiz at NutriLiving.com.

02

Add up your points within each color category and consult the Score Card on page 31 to find out which color category (or categories) will most benefit your body! Then read on to your recommended color section and learn how to formulate your NutriBlasts and **SouperBlasts** according to your specific health needs!

THE QUIZ

01 WHAT IS YOUR SEX?

	RED	ORANGE	YELLOW	GREEN	BLUE
○ Male					
○ Female					

02 WHAT IS YOUR AGE?

○ 21 and under					
○ 22-34					
○ 35-44	5				
○ 45-54	10				
○ 55-64	15				
○ 65+	15				

03 WHAT IS YOUR ETHNICITY?

○ White					
○ Hispanic or Latino			5		
○ Black or African American			5		
○ Native American or American Indian					
○ Asian / Pacific Islander			5		
○ Other					

04 HOW OFTEN DO YOU DRINK ALCOHOL?

	RED	ORANGE	YELLOW	GREEN	BLUE
◯ Never					
◯ Seldom					
◯ Sometimes				5	
◯ Often	5			10	
◯ Everyday	10			20	

05 HOW OFTEN DO YOU SMOKE?

	RED	ORANGE	YELLOW	GREEN	BLUE
◯ Never					
◯ Previous smoker	10			10	10
◯ Current smoker	20			20	20

06 HOW OFTEN DO YOU FEEL STRESSED?

	RED	ORANGE	YELLOW	GREEN	BLUE
◯ Never					
◯ Seldom					5
◯ Sometimes	5				10
◯ Often	10				15
◯ Everyday	15				20

07 HOW OFTEN DO YOU FEEL DOWN, DEPRESSED, OR HOPELESS?

	RED	ORANGE	YELLOW	GREEN	BLUE
Never					
Seldom					5
Sometimes					10
Often	5				15
Everyday	10				20

08 DO YOU HAVE TROUBLE SLEEPING?

	RED	ORANGE	YELLOW	GREEN	BLUE
Never					
Seldom					
Sometimes	5				5
Often	10		5		10
Everyday	20		10		15

09 HAVE YOU EVER BEEN DIAGNOSED WITH MIGRAINES?

	RED	ORANGE	YELLOW	GREEN	BLUE
Yes			10		20
No					

10 HOW OFTEN DO YOU GET HEADACHES?

		RED	ORANGE	YELLOW	GREEN	BLUE
○	Never					
○	Seldom			5		**5**
○	Sometimes			10		**10**
○	Often			15		**15**
○	Everyday			20		**20**

11 HOW OFTEN DO YOU TAKE MEDICATION TO CONTROL YOUR HEADACHES?

		RED	ORANGE	YELLOW	GREEN	BLUE
○	Never				10	
○	Seldom				15	
○	Sometimes				20	
○	Often					
○	Everyday					

12 DO YOU EXPERIENCE PAIN THAT PREVENTS YOU FROM DOING DAILY ACTIVITIES, SUCH AS COOKING, CLEANING, OR GETTING DRESSED?

		RED	ORANGE	YELLOW	GREEN	BLUE
○	Never					
○	Seldom			5		5
○	Sometimes			10		10
○	Often			15		15
○	Everyday			20		20

13 IN THE PAST MONTH, HAVE YOU EXPERIENCED INCREASED FATIGUE, STIFFNESS, SORENESS, SENSITIVITY TO PRESSURE, OR FEELINGS OF DEPRESSION FOR NO APPARENT REASON?

○	Never					
○	Seldom			5		5
○	Sometimes			10		10
○	Often			15		15
○	Everyday			20		20

14 HOW MUCH WEIGHT ARE YOU INTERESTED IN LOSING?

	RED	ORANGE	YELLOW	GREEN	BLUE
○ None					
○ 1-5 lbs.				5	
○ 6-20 lbs.			5	10	
○ 21-50 lbs.			10	15	
○ 51-100 lbs.			15	20	
○ 101+ lbs.			20	25	

15 HOW MUCH NATURAL, UNPROCESSED FRUIT IS IN YOUR DAILY DIET?

	RED	ORANGE	YELLOW	GREEN	BLUE
○ I eat fruit numerous times throughout the day.		5			
○ I eat fruit numerous times throughout the week.		10			
○ I rarely eat fruit.	10	15			
○ I never eat fruit.	20	20			

16 HOW MANY NATURAL, UNPROCESSED VEGETABLES ARE IN YOUR DAILY DIET?

	RED	ORANGE	YELLOW	GREEN	BLUE
I eat vegetables numerous times throughout the day.		5			
I eat vegetables numerous times throughout the week.		10	5		
I rarely eat vegetables.	10	15	10		
I never eat vegetables.	20	20	15		

17 HOW OFTEN DO YOU EXERCISE?

	RED	ORANGE	YELLOW	GREEN	BLUE
Never	20	10	10		
Seldom	15	5	5		
Sometimes	10				
Often	5	5	5		
Everyday		10	10		

18 HOW OFTEN DO YOU EXPERIENCE SHORTNESS OF BREATH?

	RED	ORANGE	YELLOW	GREEN	BLUE
Never					
Seldom					
Sometimes			5		
Often			10		
Everyday			15		

19 I OFTEN FEEL RESTLESS AT BEDTIME.

	RED	ORANGE	YELLOW	GREEN	BLUE
○ Never					
○ Seldom					
○ Sometimes		5		5	5
○ Often		10		10	10
○ Everyday		20		15	15

20 IT TAKES ME _____ TO FALL ASLEEP.

	RED	ORANGE	YELLOW	GREEN	BLUE
○ Less than 30 minutes.					5
○ Between 30 minutes and an hr.				5	10
○ Between 1 and 2 hrs.				10	15
○ Between 2 and 3 hrs.				15	20
○ More than 3 hrs.				20	25

21 HAVE YOU EVER BEEN DIAGNOSED WITH INSOMNIA?

	RED	ORANGE	YELLOW	GREEN	BLUE
○ Yes	5	5			10
○ No					

22 I OFTEN WAKE UP FEELING TIRED, DROWSY, AND WITH NO ENERGY.

		RED	ORANGE	YELLOW	GREEN	BLUE
○	Strongly disagree					
○	Disagree					
○	Neither agree nor disagree					
○	Agree		5		10	5
○	Strongly agree		10		20	10

23 DOES ANYONE IN YOUR IMMEDIATE FAMILY HAVE TYPE 1 OR TYPE 2 DIABETES?

		RED	ORANGE	YELLOW	GREEN	BLUE
○	Yes	20	5	10		
○	No					
○	I don't know	10	5	5		

24 HAVE YOU EVER BEEN DIAGNOSED WITH HIGH BLOOD PRESSURE?

		RED	ORANGE	YELLOW	GREEN	BLUE
○	Yes	20			20	
○	No					
○	I don't know	10			10	

25 HAVE YOU RECENTLY EXPERIENCED ANY OF THE FOLLOWING?

		RED	ORANGE	YELLOW	GREEN	BLUE
○	Increased thirst	5		5		
○	Increased hunger	5				
○	Increased urination	5		5		
○	Suddenly feeling tired or weak	5		5		
○	Sudden weight loss	5		5		
○	None					

26 HOW OFTEN DO YOU GET INTENSE MOOD SWINGS?

○	Never					
○	Seldom					5
○	Sometimes				5	10
○	Often				10	15
○	Everyday				15	20

WOMEN ONLY

27 HOW OFTEN DO YOU EXPERIENCE HOT FLASHES OR NIGHT SWEATS?

	RED	ORANGE	YELLOW	GREEN	BLUE
Never					
Seldom					
Sometimes	10				
Often	15				
Everyday	20				

28 DO YOU EXPERIENCE IRREGULAR MENSTRUAL CYCLES?

No					
Yes				20	
Varies				10	

29 DO YOU EXPERIENCE PAINFUL PMS SYMPTOMS?

Never					
Seldom			5		
Sometimes			10	5	5
Often			15	10	10
Always			20	15	15

30 HOW OFTEN DO YOU GET SUGAR CRAVINGS?

		RED	ORANGE	YELLOW	GREEN	BLUE
○	Never					
○	Seldom				5	
○	Sometimes				10	
○	Often				15	
○	Everyday				20	

31 IN THE PAST 4 MONTHS, HAVE YOU EXPERIENCED LOWER THAN NORMAL LIBIDO?

		RED	ORANGE	YELLOW	GREEN	BLUE
○	No				5	10
○	Yes					
○	I don't know					5

NOTE: Only these two questions are for men alone.
The remainder of questions are for both men and women.

32 WHAT IS YOUR LDL CHOLESTEROL?

	RED	ORANGE	YELLOW	GREEN	BLUE
○ Below 70 mg/dL					
○ 71-100 mg/dL	**5**				
○ 101-129 mg/dL	**10**				
○ 130-159 mg/dL	**15**				
○ 160+ mg/dL	**20**				
○ I don't know	**10**				

33 WHAT IS YOUR BLOOD PRESSURE?

	RED	ORANGE	YELLOW	GREEN	BLUE
○ Less than 120 over 80 (120/80)					
○ 120-139 over 80-89	**10**	5			
○ 140-159 over 90-99	**15**	10			
○ 160 and above over 100 and above	**20**	15			
○ I don't know	**5**	5			

34 HAVE YOU EVER SUFFERED FROM A HEART ATTACK OR STROKE?

	RED	ORANGE	YELLOW	GREEN	BLUE
○ Yes	**20**		10		**10**
○ No					
○ I don't know					

35 HOW MANY SERVINGS OF RED OR PROCESSED MEAT (INCLUDING BEEF, PORK AND DELI-STYLE LUNCH MEATS) DO YOU CONSUME IN A WEEK?

		RED	ORANGE	YELLOW	GREEN	BLUE
◯	1 serving or less					
◯	2 servings	5				5
◯	3 servings	10				10
◯	4 servings	15				15
◯	5 or more servings	20				20

36 HOW OFTEN DO YOU TAKE ASPIRIN, IBUPROFEN, OR GENERAL PAIN RELIEVERS FOR ACHES AND PAINS?

		RED	ORANGE	YELLOW	GREEN	BLUE
◯	Never					
◯	Seldom			5	5	
◯	Sometimes			10	10	
◯	Often			15	15	
◯	Everyday			20	20	

37 I NOW STRUGGLE TO DO
THE ACTIVITIES I ONCE
USED TO LOVE (WALKING,
SHOPPING, HOUSEHOLD
CHORES, ETC.)

	RED	ORANGE	YELLOW	GREEN	BLUE
○ Strongly disagree					
○ Disagree					
○ Neither agree nor disagree					
○ Agree		10	10		
○ Strongly agree		15	20		

38 I HAVE SORENESS OR
SWELLING IN ONE OR
MORE JOINTS.

	RED	ORANGE	YELLOW	GREEN	BLUE
○ Strongly disagree					
○ Disagree					
○ Neither agree nor disagree					
○ Agree			10	5	
○ Strongly agree			20	10	

39 I HAVE PERSISTENT PAIN OR STIFFNESS AFTER GETTING OUT OF BED IN THE MORNING.

	RED	ORANGE	YELLOW	GREEN	BLUE
Strongly disagree					
Disagree					
Neither agree nor disagree					
Agree		5	10		
Strongly agree		10	20		

40 I AM CONCERNED WITH THE APPEARANCE OF MY SKIN, HAIR AND/OR NAILS.

	RED	ORANGE	YELLOW	GREEN	BLUE
Strongly disagree					
Disagree					
Neither agree nor disagree					
Agree	15			15	5
Strongly agree	20			20	10

41 I AM CONCERNED WITH LOOKING OLDER THAN MY AGE.

		RED	ORANGE	YELLOW	GREEN	BLUE
○	Strongly disagree					
○	Disagree					
○	Neither agree nor disagree					
○	Agree	15		10	15	
○	Strongly agree	20		15	20	

42 I SUFFER FROM ACNE, OILY AND CLOGGED SKIN, OR OTHER SKIN ISSUES.

○	Strongly disagree					
○	Disagree					
○	Neither agree nor disagree					
○	Agree	5		10	15	
○	Strongly agree	10		15	20	

43 HOW OFTEN DO YOU EXPERIENCE GAS OR BLOATING?

○	Never					
○	Seldom					
○	Sometimes				5	
○	Often				10	
○	Everyday				15	

44 HOW OFTEN DO YOU HAVE A BOWEL MOVEMENT?

		RED	ORANGE	YELLOW	GREEN	BLUE
○	Less than 2 times per week			15	20	
○	Between 2-4 times per week			10	15	
○	Between 5-7 times per week			5	10	
○	Between 8-12 times per week				5	
○	Two or more times per day					

45 HOW OFTEN DO YOU EXPERIENCE HEARTBURN?

		RED	ORANGE	YELLOW	GREEN	BLUE
○	Never					
○	Seldom			5		
○	Sometimes			10		
○	Often			15		
○	Everyday			20		

TOTALS

SCORE CARD

1 "SERVING" OF FRUIT = 2 TBSP

Add this amount of fruit in addition to your baseline leafy greens
for your perfect, personally-formulated recipe.

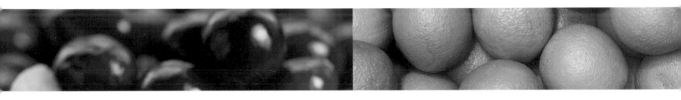

REDS
HEART HEALTH & ANTI-AGING

SCORE	SERVINGS
0-37	0
38-111	1
112-185	2
186-259	3
260-370	4

See **PAGE 37** to learn how the "reds"
can supercharge your Blasts *and*
your health!

ORANGES
IMMUNITY

SCORE	SERVINGS
0-11	0
12-34	1
35-57	2
58-80	3
81-115	4

See **PAGE 47** to learn how the
"oranges" can supercharge your Blasts
and your health!

SCORE CARD

1 "SERVING" OF FRUIT = 2 TBSP

Add this amount of fruit in addition to your baseline leafy greens
for your perfect, personally-formulated recipe.

YELLOWS
INFLAMMATION

SCORE	SERVINGS
0-36	0
37-109	1
110-182	2
182-255	3
256-365	4

See **PAGE 59** to learn how the
"yellows" can supercharge your Blasts
and your health!

GREENS
DETOX

SCORE	SERVINGS
0-36	0
37-108	1
109-181	2
182-253	3
254-360	4

See **PAGE 71** to learn how the
"greens" can supercharge your Blasts
and your health!

BLUES
BRAIN & CENTRAL NERVOUS SYSTEM

SCORE	SERVINGS
0-30	0
31-90	1
91-150	2
151-210	3
211-300	4

See **PAGE 81** to learn how the "blues" can supercharge your Blasts *and* your health!

COLOR GUIDE

THE ANTI-AGING REDS

YOUTHFUL

SEEING RED ISN'T ALWAYS A BAD THING.
In the case of diet and nutrition, red pigmentation often indicates a special blend of vitamins, minerals, and antioxidant nutrients that can help to protect the body from certain stressors associated with aging.

While the phrase "anti-aging" generally brings about images of mythical fountains of youth and magical elixirs, there is concrete evidence supporting the powerful role nutrition can play in slowing, and in some cases, reversing the wear and tear of time on the body.

Consult your quiz results to determine how many additional servings of "red" foods are recommended to incorporate into your **Nutri-Blast Rx's** or **SouperBlasts** to suit your health needs, and choose from the following list. See the end of this section for recipe ideas.

THE FOODS LISTED IN THIS SECTION CAN BE CONSIDERED "ANTI-AGING" FOODS FOR ONE OF TWO REASONS:

01

They support a healthy cardiovascular system, which is responsible for delivering oxygen and nutrients to and from every cell in the body.

02

They contain powerful phytochemicals and antioxidants—namely proanthocyanin, lycopene, and resveratrol—that have been linked to reducing and reversing oxidative stress in the body—a condition widely believed to accelerate the aging process.

In addition to foods that appear red physically, there are several foods listed in this section that are not necessarily red in color, but provide similar benefits.

TOP 10
ANTI-AGING
REDS:

01 APPLE

Apples are rich in antioxidant nutrients—specifically flavonoids, which have been shown to neutralize the effects of oxidative stress on the body. Flavonoids are also linked with cardiovascular support, and may help to protect against clogged arteries, regulate blood pressure, and improve circulation.

02 CRANBERRY

Cranberries have long been hailed for their vitamin C content and urinary tract protection, but recent laboratory experiments have linked the small red fruits to increased lifespan. While these findings are not yet conclusive in humans, there's no question that this antioxidant-rich superfood makes an excellent addition to the diet.

03 GOJI BERRIES

Also known and sold as the wolfberry, this antioxidant powerhouse is renowned for slowing the aging process, protecting the brain, and defending the body against disease. The goji berry's vitamin A content boosts immune response and eye health, and helps to prevent heart disease.

05 RED BELL PEPPER

Bell peppers are high in antioxidant carotenoids, which are highly regarded for their eye health-supporting and disease-fighting properties. Red bell peppers also contain vitamins A, C, and E, which provide a wide range of free-radical-fighting and immune-boosting benefits.

04 POMEGRANATE

Pomegranate was one of the first fruits to be deemed a "superfood," and for good reason: the small seeds of this ancient fruit are filled with polyphenol antioxidants, which have been shown to support the prevention of heart disease and certain cancers.

06 STRAWBERRY

Strawberries rank among the highest antioxidant fruits on the planet, making them excellent protectors against oxidative stress in the body, a condition often associated with aging, heart disease, and the development of cancer cells.

07 TOMATO

This popular fruit is well known for its antioxidant phytonutrient content, particularly its concentration of lycopene. Lycopene has been linked with a variety of health benefits, including protection against UV radiation and certain cancers. Tomatoes are also thought to play a role in heart health, and consumption of them has been linked to lower levels of LDL cholesterol and triglycerides in the blood.

08 ALMONDS

Filled with monounsaturated fats, fiber, and the nutrients biotin and vitamin E, almonds provide a slew of heart protecting and blood sugar-regulating benefits. Additionally, almonds have been shown to be helpful in lowering the risk of weight gain, despite their relatively high caloric content. This may be due to their satiating properties and their stabilizing effect on blood sugar levels.

9 CACAO

Raw cacao ranks among the highest antioxidant foods in the world and is well-regarded for its role in supporting heart health, balancing blood sugar levels, and regulating mood and alertness. In addition to its high concentration of antioxidant flavonoids, cacao also contains magnesium, chromium, iron, manganese, phosphorus, zinc, and copper—minerals that assist in metabolic functioning, muscular contraction, and the transportation of oxygen through the blood stream.

10 GREEN TEA

Loaded with antioxidant polyphenol and catechin compounds, green tea is one of the most healthful drinks on the planet.

Regular consumption of green tea has been linked to benefits ranging from cancer prevention to weight loss. Green tea is also known for its neurological benefits, and several studies have found a connection between the polyphenols in green tea and protection against degenerative brain conditions like Parkinson's and Alzheimer's diseases.

ADDITIONAL:
SUPERFOOD
BEAUTY BOOST

For even more anti-aging red power, add a serving of our SuperFoods Beauty Boost formula to your **NutriBlast Rx**! Loaded with exotic, high-antioxidant fruits like acerola, mangosteen, and lingonberry, as well as well-known flavonoid powerhouses like raspberries, beets, and pomegranate, among others, this powdered SuperBoost adds another dimension to your daily dose of Reds!

RED RECIPES

SERVES:
2

**TOTAL FRUIT/
VEGETABLE
SERVINGS:**
10

ALL
VEGGED
OUT
(our version of V8)

2 cups Romaine lettuce

2 tomatoes

1 cup carrot chunks

½ cup broccoli florets

½ red bell pepper

1 small beet

    (raw or steamed)

½ cup red grapes *(optional)*

    (choose frozen for a chilled Blast)

2 cups water

1 Tbsp SuperFood SuperReds *(optional)*

Add all ingredients to the **NutriBullet Rx
Short Cup** and **extract** until smooth.

SERVES:
2

**TOTAL FRUIT/
VEGETABLE
SERVINGS:**
6

YOUNG AT HEART

2 cups spinach

1 frozen medium banana

1 cup raspberries

¼ cup dried goji berries

2 Tbsp cacao powder

1 tablespoon almond butter

2 cups unsweetened vanilla almond milk

1 Tbsp SuperFood SuperReds *(optional)*

Add all ingredients to the **NutriBullet Rx Short Cup** and **extract** until smooth.

RUBY SIPPER

2 cups Red Swiss chard

2 small Red beets

   (raw or steamed)

½ cup pure pomegranate juice

1 banana

¼ cup almonds

½ tsp fresh lemon juice

2 cups water

3 to 5 ice cubes

1 Tbsp SuperFood SuperReds *(optional)*

Add all ingredients to the **NutriBullet Rx Short Cup** and **extract** until smooth.

COMFORTING TOMATO BASIL

SERVES:
4-6

TOTAL FRUIT/ VEGETABLE SERVINGS:
5

5 medium tomatoes, chopped

1 garlic clove, skin on

½ cup raw cashews

¼ cup fresh basil leaves, loosely packed

¼ tsp dried thyme

½ tsp Himalayan salt

1 tbsp chia seeds

2 cups plain, unsweetened almond milk

Add all ingredients to the **SouperBlast Pitcher** and **extract** on the **7-Minute Heated Cycle.**

THE
IMMUNE-
BOOSTING
ORANGES

IMMUNITY

THE IMMUNE SYSTEM ACTS AS THE FIRST LINE OF DEFENSE against harmful invaders like viruses and illness-causing bacteria, and as "damage control" for the entire body—helping to heal and repair infection or disease-induced harm. Immune responses involve a complex array of bodily processes that require nutritional compounds in order to function.

The nutrients commonly found in orange foods have long been associated with immune support. Case in point: oranges. The citrus fruit and its juice are frequently praised for their immune-boosting vitamin C content. However, oranges and vitamin C provide only a small slice of a deliciously varied array of immune-supporting foods.

Most notably, Vitamin A, the B-vitamins, Vitamin D, Vitamin E, selenium, and zinc contribute directly to the immune response, and

> " Most notably, Vitamin A, the B-vitamins, Vitamin D, Vitamin E, selenium, and zinc contribute directly to the immune response. "

are abundant in many of your favorite fruits, vegetables, nuts, seeds, and superfoods.

If your quiz results suggest that you could use an extra few servings of "orange" foods in your diet, check out the following pages for a guide to the top 10 foods for immunity, as well as a list of recipes that are far tastier and healthier than that glass of OJ.

The "orange" foods included in this section contain exceptional amounts of the aforementioned nutrients. Add them to your **NutriBlast Rx** and **SouperBlasts** during cold and flu season, or at any time you start to feel under the weather.

TOP 10
IMMUNE-
BOOSTING
ORANGES:

01 CAMU CAMU

Native to the Amazon region, camu camu contains one of nature's highest concentrations of vitamin C. Perhaps the most well-known immunity-boosting nutrient, vitamin C has antioxidant, antibacterial, and antiviral properties. Including camu-camu in your daily regimen, especially during cold and flu season, can help your body build its defenses against harmful invaders.

02 CARROT

Carrots are highly regarded for their beta-carotene content, an antioxidant carotenoid that the body converts into vitamin A. Vitamin A has been found to play a role in protecting the body against infection, and also supports vision, bone, and skin health.

03 ORANGE

Oranges have long been hailed as the go-to immune-boosting fruit, and for good reason. This juicy citrus is filled with vitamin C, as well as fiber, folate, vitamin B1, and potassium. They also taste delicious, making them an easy choice for immune-boosting Blasting!

04 ORANGE BELL PEPPER

Much like carrots, orange bell peppers are loaded with carotenoids—specifically, alpha carotene, beta-carotene, lutein, and lycopene, among others—all of which have immune, heart, and vision-supporting properties. Bell peppers also contain vitamin C, which can help protect the body against infection.

05 RED LENTIL

Lentils contain a wealth of nutrients, including vitamin B6, zinc, and iron—all of which play an important role in immune support. Vitamin B6 and zinc, in particular, help the body manufacture white blood cells—an integral part of the immune response.

06 SWEET POTATO

Nutritionally similar to carrots, sweet potatoes contain a wealth of beta-carotene and vitamin A, which work together to fight oxidative stress in the body that often results from infection or disease. Sweet potatoes also contain several other beneficial antioxidant nutrients. It is advisable that you pair sweet potatoes with a small amount of healthful plant-based fats—roughly 3-5 grams—to maximize your body's absorption of beta-carotene.

07 BRAZIL NUT

This large tree nut is one of nature's best sources of selenium—a nutrient which helps produce proteins that prompt the immune response. Just one Brazil nut contains the daily requirement of selenium; including just one per day in your **NutriBlast Rx** or **SouperBlast** can help prepare your body for battle against the many invaders it encounters on a daily basis.

08 CAULIFLOWER

Cauliflower makes an excellent immune boosting food due to its many antioxidants, including glutathione, which fights harmful bacteria in the body to protect against infection. Cauliflower also contains folate—a B-vitamin necessary for the production of invader-fighting white blood cells. Enjoy raw in a **NutriBlast Rx** or **SouperBlast** to enjoy the many health benefits this veggie provides.

09 GARLIC

This pungent little plant is known for its immune-boosting prowess. Home to hundreds of sulfuric compounds, garlic has been studied for its antibacterial and antiviral qualities, and has been used as remedy for infections ranging from gangrene to the common cold throughout the course of history. It certainly packs a punch of flavor, but adding a clove or two of raw garlic to your **SouperBlasts** might be the secret to warding off those sniffles come cold and flu season.

10 ONION

Much like garlic, onion contains sulfuric compounds that have proven to be helpful in fighting infection. Onions also contain prebiotic compounds, which feed the good bacteria in your gut that ease digestion.

ORANGE
RECIPES

SERVES:
2

**TOTAL FRUIT/
VEGETABLE
SERVINGS:**
7

SWEET
PAPAYA
PUNCH

2 cups Swiss chard

1½ cups papaya

1 medium steamed sweet potato

2 Tbsp almond butter

2 tsp cinnamon

2 cups water

Add all ingredients to the **NutriBullet Rx
Short Cup** and **extract** until smooth.

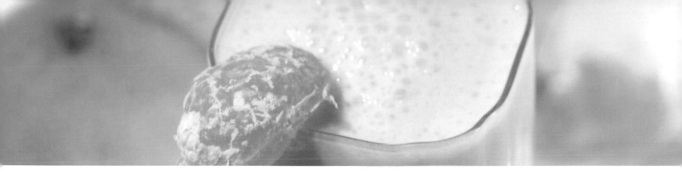

SERVES:
2

**TOTAL FRUIT/
VEGETABLE
SERVINGS:**
6.5

MORNING STAR

2 cups spinach

1½ bananas

2 Tbsp pumpkin seeds

1 orange

2 medium carrot sticks

2 Tbsp plant-based protein powder

(**OR** one scoop as provided by brand)

2 cups unsweetened vanilla almond milk

Add all ingredients to the **NutriBullet Rx Short Cup** and **extract** until smooth.

SERVES:
2

**TOTAL FRUIT/
VEGETABLE
SERVINGS:**
7

SLIMMING VITAMIN C-ITRUS

2 cups spinach

½ cup broccoli florets

½ cup mango

1 medium orange

4 medium strawberries

½ cup raspberries

2 Tbsp chia seeds

2 cups water

Add all ingredients to the **NutriBullet Rx Short Cup** and **extract** until smooth.

SWEET & SPICY CARROT

SERVES:
4-6

TOTAL FRUIT/ VEGETABLE SERVINGS:
10

1 tbsp minced shallot

½ tsp minced fresh ginger

2 cups carrots, cut into coins

2 cups cauliflower,
washed, drained, and finely chopped

1 medium baked or steamed sweet potato,
peeled and cut into chunks

2 cups vegetable broth

2 tsp lemon juice

½ tsp ground turmeric

1/8 tsp cayenne pepper

½ tsp sea salt

1/3 cup caramelized yellow onion *(optional)*

Add all ingredients to the **SouperBlast Pitcher** and **extract** on the **7-Minute Heated Cycle.**

SERVES:
4-6

TOTAL FRUIT/
VEGETABLE
SERVINGS:
6-8

GARLIC ROASTED BUTTERNUT SQUASH

2 tbsp olive oil

3 garlic cloves, minced

3 tbsp fresh parsley

10 fresh sage leaves,
   rinsed, dried, and chopped

1 tsp salt

3 lbs butternut squash,
   about 1½ medium squash,
   peeled and cut into 1-inch cubes

1 ½ cups chicken or vegetable broth *

TIP: Many stores offer frozen butternut squash. Prepare as it appears on the bag. Mix with herbs and broth and blend.

* Cooled to room temperature for at least 30 minutes, if making it fresh!

1 Preheat oven to 400 degrees.

2 Mix olive oil, garlic, parsley, sage, and salt together.

3 Add the prepared squash and toss to coat.

4 Transfer the mixture to a baking dish and roast for 50-55 minutes until the squash is tender. **Remove from the oven and allow to cool to room temperature for at least 30 minutes.** You can accelerate this process by refrigerating the squash for 10-20 minutes.

5 Transfer the cooked squash to the **SouperBlast Pitcher.** Add the broth and **extract** the mixture on the **7-minute Heating Cycle.**

THE INFLAMMATION-SOOTHING YELLOWS

RECOVERY

IF YOU'VE EVER ENJOYED A DELICIOUS BOWL OF INDIAN CURRY, you are most likely familiar with turmeric—the spice that gives traditional curry its glowing yellow color. Turmeric is one of nature's most potent anti-inflammatory foods due to its concentrated content of the phenol circumin, and it is not the only yellow-hued food to assist in the body's regulation of inflammation.

Studies show that consuming foods rich in yellow flavonoids and dark yellow carotenoids can help calm persistent inflammation in the body—a condition considered a major driver of many modern day diseases, including diabetes, cancer, heart disease, arthritis, and dementia.

To fight inflammation, it is equally as important to avoid foods in the diet that foster the condition as it is to eat foods that fight it.

> " To fight inflammation, it is equally as important to avoid foods in the diet that foster the condition as it is to eat foods that fight it. "

Fast food, fried food, processed foods, refined grains, sugar-laden desserts and soda, and alcohol all promote a cascade of reactions in the body that ultimately signal trouble.

If you scored high for yellow, your body is most likely engaged in some type of inflammatory response. To soothe your inner fire, avoid the aforementioned foods, and incorporate the "Top 10 Yellows" detailed in this section into your **NutriBlast Rx** or **SouperBlast.**

The foods listed in this section can be considered anti-inflammatory for the following reasons:

- They contain phenolic compounds and enzymes that help blunt the inflammatory response.
- They contain antioxidants that scavenge free radicals in the body, preventing them from causing further damage.
- They lower the levels of certain enzymes in the body known to cause inflammation.

TOP 10
INFLAMMATION-SOOTHING
YELOWS:

01 GINGER

Known for its anti-nausea effects, ginger is also a powerful anti-inflammatory food due to its suppression of compounds known to signal the inflammatory response. There is some evidence that ginger may also help reduce pain caused by osteoarthritis (OA), but results are not yet conclusive.

02 GOLDEN BEETS

Many of the betalains found in beets function both as antioxidants and anti-inflammatory molecules. While the yellow variety is less potent than its red cousin, it's still a great (and less messy!) addition to your Blast.

03 PINEAPPLE

Pineapples contain the enzyme bromelain. Bromelain has been shown in several studies to reduce inflammation associated with arthritis, sinusitis, tendonitis, sprains, and other inflammatory conditions.

04 RAINIER CHERRIES

These sweet yellow-red cherries are bursting with polyphenolic compounds known to reduce inflammation and oxidation in the body. Specifically, numerous clinical studies have found cherries to be especially helpful in relieving the muscular damage and inflammation that follow vigorous exercise.

05 SAFFRON

Though saffron is known primarily as one of the world's most expensive flavor-enhancing spices, it has been used for centuries in Asia as a medicinal plant. Its antioxidant and scavenging properties help the body fight against pro-inflammatory cytokine proteins and various free radicals.

06 TURMERIC

Turmeric is one of the most celebrated anti-inflammatory foods due its high concentrations of the compound circumin, which gives the root its intense yellow color. Circumin has been found to reduce the levels of two enzymes in the body that cause inflammation, and has proven especially effective in soothing arthritic symptoms.

07 VIRGIN OLIVE OIL

Olive oil is rich in Vitamin E, a powerful antioxidant shown to spur anti-inflammatory activity in tissues. Additionally, studies have revealed that a compound in the oil prevents the body from releasing two pro-inflammatory enzymes: COX-1 and COX-2, which can cause pain in the body when produced in excess.

09 FLAX SEEDS

Flax seeds are a rich source of ALA Omega-3 fatty acids, which have been shown to significantly reduce the concentration of pro-inflammatory compounds in the blood. The benefits of flax seed are only available to the body in powdered form, making the **NutriBullet Rx** the perfect tool for enjoying this healthful food!

08 YELLOW CHILI PEPPER

Chili peppers are rich in capsaicin, a chemical used in topical creams to reduce pain and inflammation. Adding a small piece or two into your **NutriBlast Rx** or **SouperBlast** can help to heal your insides as well! Just use caution with your serving size…a little bit of this potent pepper goes a long way!

10 KIWI

Though its flesh is green, kiwi earns its spot on the list of "Top 10 Yellows" due to its inflammation-reducing properties. Like pineapple, kiwi contains a beneficial protein-digesting enzyme that boosts the body's ability to fight inflammation. It is also bursting with vitamin C.

YELLOW
RECIPES

SERVES:

2

TOTAL FRUIT/ VEGETABLE SERVINGS:

7

BEST BLAST EVER

2 cups spinach

1 frozen banana

1 cup peach slices

1 cup frozen pineapple

2 Tbsp unsweetened coconut flakes

2 small drops pure vanilla extract

¼ tsp cinnamon

1 cup coconut water

1 cup unsweetened almond milk

Add all ingredients to the **NutriBullet Rx Short Cup** and **extract** until smooth.

CHERRY ON TOP

SERVES:

2

TOTAL FRUIT/ VEGETABLE SERVINGS:

5

2 cups spinach

1 banana

1 cup Rainier cherries — pitted

(may sub frozen cherries)

¼ cup walnuts

½ inch fresh ginger

2 cups unsweetened vanilla almond milk

Add all ingredients to the **NutriBullet Rx Short Cup** and **extract** until smooth.

INFLAMED NO MORE

SERVES:

2

TOTAL FRUIT/ VEGETABLE SERVINGS:

5;

6

IF INCLUDNG WHEATGRASS

2 cups spinach

Pinch of whole wheatgrass *OR*

2 tsp wheatgrass powder

(**2** Tbsp wheatgrass juice

may also be used)

½ cup pineapple chunks

1 banana

20 walnut halves

1 Tbsp flax seeds

½ cup Rainier cherries — pitted

(may sub frozen cherries)

2 cups brewed and chilled green tea

Add all ingredients to the **NutriBullet Rx Short Cup** and **extract** until smooth.

TURMERIFIC

2 cups spinach

1 cup diced pineapple

½ cup diced papaya

¼ lime

¼ lemon

½ cup grapefruit slices

1 Tbsp flax seeds

½ tsp turmeric powder

2 cups water

TOTAL FRUIT/ VEGETABLE SERVINGS:
7

Add all ingredients to the **NutriBullet Rx Short Cup** and **extract** until smooth.

SERVES:
4-6

TOTAL FRUIT/
VEGETABLE
SERVINGS:
5

COCONUT CURRY PUMPKIN SOUP

2 cups roasted pumpkin *

    (may also used canned

    pure pumpkin puree)

1 Tbsp cold pressed coconut oil

1/3 cup (about 1/8th) yellow onion

    (chopped)

½ medium sweet apple

    (core and seeds removed)

½ clove garlic

    (**OR** 1-2 cloves roasted garlic)

1 tsp curry powder

¼ tsp nutmeg

1 cup vegetable broth *

1 cup light coconut milk

salt and pepper to taste

* **Cooled to room temperature for at least 30 minutes, if making it fresh!**

1. If using roasted pumpkin: Cut pumpkin into large chunks. Place into a ziplock bag and drizzle in olive oil and salt. Shake until fully coated with oil. Place onto baking sheet and roast on 400 degrees F in the oven for about 30-40 min or until soft and fork-tender. **Allow to cool for 30 min to room temperature.** You can accelerate this process by refrigerating the pumpkin for 10-20 minutes.

2. Add all ingredients to the **SouperBlast Pitcher,** screw on the **Vent Top**, and **extract** until smooth and warm.

3. Flavanoid-rich cherries combine with the omega-3 fatty acids found in walnuts and the zing of ginger to create this delicious, inflammation-fighting NutriBlast.

THE DETOXIFYING GREENS

REFRESH

DETOXIFICATION IS A NATURAL BODILY PROCESS and most organ systems have developed their own methods of self-cleansing. However, in our modern era, our exposure to environmental, chemical, dietary, and even emotional toxins is greater than ever before and most bodies could do with a little external assistance.

If the concept of "detoxing" terrifies you, have no fear! Our methods of detoxification do not involve forgoing all food in favor of overpriced green elixirs or soaking in an Epson salt bath for the larger portion of the day. If your quiz results skewed green, all we suggest is that you toss some of the green cleansing foods detailed in this section into your **NutriBlasts Rx's** and **SouperBlasts** in addition to your baseline leafy greens.

Green foods contain chlorophyll, a pigment responsible for their green color and a critical component of the photosynthetic process. Chlorophyll has been shown to neutralize free radicals and eliminate toxins like heavy metals, pesticides, and industrial pollutants from the body, making it an essential addition to the diet in our increasingly toxic environment.

Despite a survey showing that 28% of Americans "fear the [way they] look," green juices and smoothies have never been more popular. If you believe in the power of green as strongly as we do, the **NutriBullet Rx** is your ideal tool, helping you maximize your intake of leafy greens and cruciferous veggies without spending a fortune at the juice bar or smoothie shop. Choose from a wide array of delicious and satisfying **NutriBlast Rx** and **SouperBlast** recipes and kiss those toxins goodbye! We promise you won't miss them.

Consult your quiz results to determine how many additional servings of "green" foods are recommended to incorporate into your **NutriBlast Rx** or **SouperBlasts** to suit your health needs and choose from the following list. See the end of this section for recipe ideas.

The foods listed in this section can be considered detoxifying for the following reasons:

- They contain certain molecules that bind carcinogens and other internal toxins together to prepare for excretion.

- They provide critical nutrients for the liver's natural detoxification pathways.

- They contain phytochemicals such as Indole-3-Carbinol (I3C), which appear to have anti-carcinogenic and anti-cancer properties.

- They promote acid/alkaline balance that can lead to more effective elimination of toxins from the body.

TOP 10
DETOXIFYING
GREENS:

01 ARTICHOKE

The liver detoxifies the body by filtering the blood, producing bile, and breaking down toxins and waste. Artichokes have been shown in human studies to increase the production of bile, which helps to eliminate toxins in the body by flushing them out through the colon.

02 BROCCOLI

A member of the brassica family, broccoli is rich in sulfur-containing compounds known as glucosinates. Human studies show that glucosinate-containing compounds may trigger detoxifying enzyme systems in the body. Increasing consumption of glucosinates may help to fuel this process.

03 BRUSSELS SPROUTS

Like broccoli, Brussels sprouts are also a member of the brassica family, and are also rich in sulfer-containing glucosinates. Brussels sprouts contain compounds shown to be helpful in both Phase 1 and Phase 2 of the detoxification process, supplying ample antioxidant support during the former, and liver support during the latter.

04 CILANTRO AND PARSLEY

Proving that great things come in small packages, these herbs are known for their heavy-metal chelating capabilities—meaning they help bind metal ions for easier elimination from the body.

05 CHLORELLA

This single-celled algae has been shown to bind heavy metals such as mercury and other toxic pollutants together to escort them out of vital tissues. Chlorella is noted for its large amounts of chlorophyll, which is why one tiny scoop will make your entire **NutriBlast Rx** glow green!

06 GREEN TEA

Green tea is rich in antioxidants known as catechins. These have shown to boost liver function and help reduce fat storage in the liver.

07 KALE

Kale is one of the top detoxifying greens for a number of reasons: it contains ample antioxidants, which neutralize toxic free radical compounds in the body; it is highly fibrous and improves bowel regularity, which facilitates elimination of bulk and toxins from the colon; and, as a member of the brassica family, it is filled with compounds known to support healthy liver functioning.

08 RED BEETS & THEIR GREENS

Beets are not green, you're correct, but they are hugely helpful when it comes to detoxification. The deep red root and its leafy tops contain betalins—compounds with powerful antioxidant properties that also support Phase 2 Detoxification in the liver.

09 WHEATGRASS

Wheatgrass contains multiple enzymes, minerals, and vitamins, as well as our beloved chlorophyll that aid the body's natural ability to cleanse itself. While the mechanism isn't exactly known, it is believed that since the chlorophyll molecule is similar in structure to hemoglobin, it helps boost blood flow which aids in general detoxification.

10 LEMONS

Though yellow in color, lemons rightly deserve their place among the "Top-10 Greens" with their detoxifying properties. Lemon juice helps to balance pH levels in body and, like artichokes, stimulates the production of bile from the liver, which helps to bind and remove toxins from the body.

ADDITIONAL:
SUPERFOOD CLEANSING GREENS

Bursting with chlorophyll-rich, detoxifying superfoods like chlorella, alfalfa, spirulina, and wheatgrass, this wonderful mixture combines the world's most powerful greens in easy-to-Blast powdered form! Cleansing, rejuvenating, and mighty tasty—thanks to the addition of organic vanilla and cinnamon—the SuperFood Cleansing Greens formula makes a great addition to any **NutriBlast Rx**.

GREEN RECIPES

SERVES:

2

TOTAL FRUIT/ VEGETABLE SERVINGS:

7

GREEN FOOD LOVER'S BLAST

1 cup baby kale

1 cup spinach

¼ cup sliced cucumber

¼ cup sliced zucchini

2 medium celery stalks

1 cup fresh pineapple

¼ cup fresh parsley

2 Tbsp chia seeds

2 tsp chlorella powder

1 cup coconut water

1 cup brewed green tea (chilled)

1 Tbsp SuperFood SuperGreens *(optional)*

Add all ingredients to the **NutriBullet Rx Short Cup** and **extract** until smooth.

GREEN DETOX MACHINE

2 cups dinosaur kale

2 green apples (core and seeds removed)

1 cup cucumber

1 celery stalk

½ cup pineapple (may sub mango)

½ lemon (peeled)

¼ cup hemp seeds

2 fresh mint leaves

1 Tbsp cold-pressed, unrefined coconut oil

1 cup coconut water

1 cup water

4-5 ice cubes

1 Tbsp SuperFood SuperGreens *(optional)*

Add all ingredients to the **NutriBullet Rx Short Cup** and **extract** until smooth.

SO FRESH &
SO CLEAN

SERVES:

2

**TOTAL FRUIT/
VEGETABLE
SERVINGS:**

8.5

2 cups Swiss chard

½ cup cucumber

2 celery stalks

¼ cup fresh parsley

½ cup carrot chunks

1 medium pear

   (core and seeds removed)

½ orange (peeled)

¼ lemon (peeled)

½ inch fresh ginger

½ cup pineapple

2 cups water

1 Tbsp SuperFood SuperGreens *(optional)*

Add all ingredients to the **NutriBullet Rx
Short Cup** and **extract** until smooth.

CLEAN SPRING SOUP

1 apple

6 stalks celery

3 cups spinach

½ cup walnuts

1 Tbsp Dijon mustard

½ tsp Himalayan salt

1 Tbsp lemon juice

2 Cups low sodium vegetable broth

Black pepper to taste

1 Tbsp SuperFood SuperGreens *(optional)*

Add all ingredients to the **SouperBlast Pitcher** and **extract** on the **7-Minute Heated Cycle.**

THE BRAIN-EMPOWERING BLUES & PURPLES

ACUITY

GETTING THE BLUES NEVER SEEMED SO SMART! Foods that are physically blue or purple in color contain a wealth of antioxidant nutrients that benefit the brain and central nervous system. In particular, anthocyanin—the antioxidant pigment that gives these foods their indigo shades—has been linked to maintaining long-term brain health, extending the sharpness of memory and overall cognitive functioning that tend to decline with age.

Anthocyanins are also known for supporting circulation in the body. A brain cannot function in the absence of nutrients and oxygen, so a consistent blood flow is integral to its health.

In addition to anthocyanin-rich blue fruits and vegetables, foods rich in DHA omega-3 fatty acids have proven effective in improving and maintaining brain health. The gray matter tissue present in our brains is largely comprised of DHA fatty acids, a substance

> " Anthocyanins are also known for supporting circulation in the body. "

the body cannot produce on its own. To receive the building blocks of this gray matter, our body must rely on food sources. Absent or decaying "gray matter" has been associated with dementia and Alzheimer's Disease, so including a hefty dose of Omega-3 fatty acids in the diet could be beneficial for aging brains.

Consult your quiz results to determine how many additional servings of "blue/purple" foods are recommended to incorporate into your **NutriBlast Rx's** or **SouperBlasts** to suit your health needs and choose from the following list. See the end of this section for recipe ideas.

TOP 10 BRAIN-EMPOWERING BLUES:

antioxidants supply a wide variety of health benefits, but they've come to recent attention for their protective effect on the brain. Though much is still being researched about anthocyanin pigments, studies suggest that they may help the brain recover from trauma and help protect against age-related brain degeneration.

01 BLACK BEANS

These popular legumes are often praised for their protein and fiber content, but what separates this variety from other beans is their rich anthocyanin content. Anthocyanin

02 BLACKBERRIES

Another anthocyanin-rich fruit, blackberries also contain healthful fiber and vitamin C. A 2009 Tufts University study found that anthocyanin-rich pigments potentially increase signaling between neurons in the brain, which could help to prevent inflammation in the brain.

03 BLUEBERRIES

Blueberries have become the poster child for the neurological benefits of anthocyanin pigments, and for good reason. Studies show that even short-term inclusion of blueberries in the diet can improve memory function in aging brains. Blueberries have also shown to have preventative effects against destructive brain processes leading to Parkinson's disease and Alzheimer's disease in several laboratory studies.

04 EGGPLANT

Like many of the foods in this section, the skin of the eggplant contains anthocyanin pigments. Specifically, the globe eggplant contains the anthocyanin nasunin, which has proven especially effective in protecting the brain's fatty tissues. Cooked eggplant makes a delicious addition to any **SouperBlast**.

05 PLUMS

While plums come in a variety of colors, those with the darkest skin and flesh are typically highest in anthocyanin antioxidants. However, all varieties provide a wealth of beneficial nutrients, and can be incorporated into **NutriBlasts Rx's** and **SouperBlasts** alike!

06 PURPLE CABBAGE

In addition to its brain-protecting anthocyanin pigments, cabbage also contains sulfuric compounds known to assist in anti-inflammatory and detoxifying processes within the body. To reap the maximum benefits from this superfood, enjoy raw in **NutriBlast Rx's** or **SouperBlasts,** or cook for less than 5 minutes.

07 PURPLE GRAPES

Like the other darkly colored foods on this list, dark purple grapes contain anthocyanin pigments shown to extend brain health with age. Additionally, grapes contain resveratrol, an antioxidant variant linked to anti-aging benefits. Generally speaking, the darker the skin and flesh of the grape, the more antioxidant-rich it will be, so look out for dark blue-black varieties like the Concord or Ribier grape.

08 AVOCADO

Avocados contain the highest concentration of healthy fats among all fruits, compounds that are essential to healthy brain development. Among these fats are Omega-3 fatty acids, which have been found play a role in reducing harmful inflammation that can impair brain and other bodily functions. In addition to their healthy fats, avocados contain vitamin E, protein, and fiber.

09 FLAX SEEDS

These seeds contain a high proportion of brain-boosting omega-3 fatty acids—over 100% of the recommended daily intake in just one 2-tbsp serving! To reap the benefits of these healthy fats, as well as the remaining nutrients locked within these somewhat slippery seeds, it is best to extract flax seeds in the **NutriBullet Rx** prior to consuming.

10 WALNUTS

These brain-shaped nuts are powerful sources of omega-3 fatty acids, which have been shown to help improve brain health and memory. In addition to their brain-boosting prowess, walnuts also contain gamma-tocopherol, an especially heart-healthy form of vitamin E.

BLUE & PURPLE RECIPES

BRAINIAC BLAST

2 cups baby kale

1½ cup frozen blueberries

1 avocado

2 Tbsp hemp seeds

1 cup coconut water

1 cup brewed green tea (chilled)

1 Tbsp lime juice

1 Tsp chlorella powder *(optional)*

6 ice cubes

Add all ingredients to the **NutriBullet Rx Short Cup** and **extract** until smooth.

SHADES OF GRAPE

SERVES:

2

TOTAL FRUIT/ VEGETABLE SERVINGS:

5

2 cups spinach

1½ cups frozen red or purple grapes

¼ cup chopped walnuts

2 dashes of cinnamon

1 cup brewed green tea (chilled)

1 cup water

Add all ingredients to the **NutriBullet Rx Short Cup** and **extract** until smooth.

BLUES
BE GONE

SERVES:
2

**TOTAL FRUIT/
VEGETABLE
SERVINGS:**
7

2 cups kale

1 cup blackberries

1 cup blueberries

1 banana

½ cup cooked black beans

¼ cup walnuts

2 Tbsp raw cacao

2 cups almond milk

Add all ingredients to the **NutriBullet Rx
Short Cup** and **extract** until smooth.

BLACK BEAN SOUP

1 Tbsp olive oil

1 medium onion, diced

2 ribs celery

1 large carrot, diced

1 clove garlic

2 15-oz cans organic black beans, divided

1 Tbsp fresh lime juice

1 tsp salt

2 tsp ground cumin

¼ tsp red pepper flakes

2 cups vegetable broth, *

    PLUS **¼** cup if necessary to
    moisten pot ingredients

¼ cup fresh cilantro, divided
    (half in soup and half as garnish)

ground pepper to taste

*** Cooled to room temperature for at
least 30 minutes, if making it fresh!**

1 Heat oil in a pot over medium heat. Add onion, celery, carrot, and garlic and sauté until tender, about 4 minutes. Add canned beans, lime juice, salt, cumin, and red pepper flakes and stir until combined and heated through, about 5 minutes. If ingredients start to stick to the pot, add up to ¼ cup of vegetable broth to moisten the mixture.

2 **Allow the pot mixture to cool to room temperature, at least 30 minutes.** You can accelerate this process by transferring to the refrigerator for 10-20 minutes

3 Add half of the sauté mixture to the **SouperBlast Pitcher** along with 2 tbsp. fresh cilantro and 2 cups vegetable broth. **Extract** on the **7-minute Heated Cycle.**

ADDITIONAL NUTRI-BULLET RX RECIPES

MORE RECIPES!

The recipes in this section are not organized by color—though you are welcome to boost them according to your specific color profile. However, they do include a wide variety of incredible fruits, vegetables, nuts, and seeds to meet a wide variety of nutritional needs. From hearty meal-replacing **NutriBlast Rx's** to nut butters, belly-warming classic soups to warm superfood elixirs, this section shows you how to make use of the full range of healthy eating options the **NutriBullet Rx** provides!

THE
HEARTY & LIGHT
NUTRI
BLAST
RX

These delicious **NutriBlast Rx's** are loaded with stick-to-your ribs fruits, vegetables, nuts, and seeds, and provide a great alternative to a standard meal. Enjoy the following recipes for a quick and incredibly nutritious breakfast, lunch, or dinner, and see how your body responds to the power of extracted nutrition!

BEAN QUEEN

SERVES:
2

2 cups kale

1½ cups blackberries

1 banana

½ cup cooked black beans

20 almonds

2 Tbsp raw cacao

2 cups water

Add all ingredients to the **NutriBullet Rx Short Cup** and **extract** until smooth.

SERVES:
2

DESSERT ROSE

2 cups mixed greens

1 frozen banana

1 cup frozen raspberries

20 hazelnuts

2 Tbsp raw cacao

1 tsp pure vanilla extract
(*OR* vanilla powder)

2 cups unsweetened
vanilla almond milk

Add all ingredients to the
NutriBullet Rx Short Cup and
extract until smooth.

TOUCH OF GRASS

SERVES:
2

Pinch of whole wheatgrass *OR*

2 tsp wheatgrass powder

(2 Tbsp wheatgrass juice

may also be used)

½ cup pineapple chunks

1 banana

20 walnut halves

1 Tbsp chia seeds

½ cup pitted cherries

2 cups brewed, chilled green tea

Add all ingredients to the
NutriBullet Rx Short Cup and
extract until smooth.

N'ZINC

SERVES:
2

2 cup baby kale

1½ bananas

2 Tbsp pumpkin seeds

2 Tbsp sesame seeds

¾ cup steel cut oats,

cooked

2 cups unsweetened

almond milk

Add all ingredients to the
NutriBullet Rx Short Cup
and **extract** until smooth.

MACARITA

SERVES:
2

2 cups Swiss chard

1½ bananas

¼ cup almonds

2-4 Tbsp plant-based protein
powder (depending on
brand) (est. 60-100 cals)

2 tsp maca powder

2 cups coconut water

Add all ingredients to the
NutriBullet Rx Short Cup
and **extract** until smooth.

BRAN NEW

SERVES:
2

2 cups baby kale

1½ bananas

1 cup raspberries

1 cup blueberries

1/3 cup wheat bran

¼ cup cashews

5 tsp raw cacao

2 cups water

Add all ingredients to the
NutriBullet Rx Short Cup and
extract until smooth.

CALCI-YUM

SERVES:
2

2 cups spinach

1½ bananas

1 orange

¼ cup almonds

1 Tbsp chia seeds

1 Tbsp blackstrap molasses

2 cups water

Add all ingredients to the
NutriBullet Rx Short Cup and
extract until smooth.

CHARD, I'M SURE

SERVES:

2

1 cup Swiss chard

1 cup kale

1 medium pear

1 cup blueberries

¼ cup cashews

½ cup dried goji berries

2 Tbsp cacao powder or nibs

2 cups unsweetened
almond milk

Add all ingredients to the
NutriBullet Rx Short Cup and
extract until smooth.

MAGNESIUM ELYSIUM

SERVES:

2

1 cup spinach

1 cup Swiss chard

2 Tbsp pumpkin seeds
(pepitas)

1 cup mango

1 cup pineapple

¼ cup cashews

2 cups coconut water

Add all ingredients to the
NutriBullet Rx Short Cup
and **extract** until smooth.

DAVID WOLFE'S BEST DAY EVER BLAST

SERVES:
2

2 bananas

2 Tbsp raw cacao powder

¼ cup dried goji berries

2 tsp raw honey

½ cup aloe vera juice

1½ cups coconut water

Add all ingredients to the **NutriBullet Rx Short Cup** and **extract** until smooth.

CARDIO PUMP

SERVES:
2

2 cups kale

2 small carrots

½ cup uncooked rolled oats (may use cooked if desired)

1 cup mixed berries

2 Tbsp chia seeds

Handful of ice

2 cups unsweetened vanilla almond milk

Add all ingredients to the **NutriBullet Rx Short Cup** and **extract** until smooth.

ALMOND ALLY

2 cups spinach

¼ cup raw almond butter

4 pitted dates

2 banana

2 cups unsweetened almond milk

Add all ingredients to the
NutriBullet Rx Short Cup and
extract until smooth.

SIPPING STEADY

2 cups spinach

2 Tbsp chia seeds

1½ Tbsp raw cacao powder

   OR nibs

2 tsp cinnamon

1 apple (cored)

½ avocado

2 cups water

Add all ingredients to the
NutriBullet Rx Short Cup and
extract until smooth.

BLOOD SUGAR BABY

2 cups Swiss chard

1 small apple

1 banana

¼ cup pumpkin seeds

¼ cup walnut halves

2 tsp Ceylon cinnamon

2 cups water

Add all ingredients to the
NutriBullet Rx Short Cup
and **extract** until smooth.

LIGHT BLASTS

Maximize your daily intake of fruits, veggies, nuts, and seeds by enjoying these light **Nu-triBlast Rx's** as a snack or side dish. Loaded with incredible extracted nutrition and tally-ing less than 200 calories per serving, these **NutriBlast Rx's** make a perfect pick-me-up any time of day!

I BRAN SO FAR

SERVES:
2

½ cup wheat bran

2 cups collard greens

1 banana

1 cup blueberries
   (may sub strawberries)

20 raw almonds

2 cups water

Add all ingredients to the **NutriBullet Rx Short Cup** and **extract** until smooth.

BROOM SERVICE

SERVES:
2

2 cups kale

6 sprigs fresh parsley

½ cup sliced cucumber

2 small stalks celery

1 pear

½ inch ginger

1 Tbsp Bragg's
apple cider vinegar

2 cups water

Add all ingredients to the
NutriBullet Rx Short Cup and **extract** until smooth.

AVOCACAO AMBROSIA

SERVES:
2

2 cups spinach

1½ cups blueberries

½ avocado

2 Tbsp raw cacao powder

2 cups water

OR coconut water

Add all ingredients to the
NutriBullet Rx Short Cup and **extract** until smooth.

SWELL SOOTHER

SERVES:
2

2 cups spinach

¾ cup blueberries

1 cup diced pineapple

1 tsp maca powder

1½ Tbsp chia seeds

2 cups water

Add all ingredients to the
NutriBullet Rx Short Cup and
extract until smooth.

GRAPE ESCAPE

SERVES:
2

2 cups spinach

1½ cup purple seedless grapes

2 Tbsp apple cider vinegar

1 cup pineapple chunks

2 Tbsp sunflower seeds

½-inch piece of fresh ginger

½ tsp cinnamon

2 cups water

Add all ingredients to the
NutriBullet Rx Short Cup and
extract until smooth.

PAPAYA PUNCH

SERVES:
2

2 cups Swiss chard

1½ cups papaya

1 small steamed sweet potato

2 Tbsp almond butter

2 tsp cinnamon

2 cups water

Add all ingredients to the
NutriBullet Rx Short Cup and
extract until smooth.

EASY CIDER

SERVES:
2

2 cups spinach

1½ bananas

2 kiwi

2 Tbsp apple cider vinegar

1 inch slice of fresh ginger

1 tsp Ceylon cinnamon

2 cups water

Add all ingredients to the
NutriBullet Rx Short Cup
and **extract** until smooth.

GINGER SNAP

2 cups butter lettuce

1½ bananas

2 small ripe pears

1 inch ginger

2 tsp Ceylon cinnamon

½ tsp nutmeg

2 cups unsweetened
   almond milk

Add all ingredients to the
NutriBullet Rx Short Cup and
extract until smooth.

SOOTHE OPERATOR

2 cups mixed lettuce

3 small celery stalks

1½ banana

1½ cups papaya
   (**OR** pineapple)

2 cups water

Add all ingredients to the
NutriBullet Rx Short Cup
and **extract** until smooth.

MOVIN' AND GROOVIN'

SERVES:
2

2 cups Swiss chard

1 small steamed sweet potato

1 cup blueberries

5 dried apricots

1 cup coconut water

1 cup water

Add all ingredients to the **NutriBullet Rx Short Cup** and **extract** until smooth.

TUMMY TAMER

SERVES:
2

2 cups spinach

¾ cup pitted cherries

¾ cup grapes

½ cup rolled oats

1 Tbsp chia seeds

½ cup pure apple juice

1½ cups water

Add all ingredients to the **NutriBullet Rx Short Cup** and **extract** until smooth.

CITRUS SLIMMER

SERVES:
2

2 cups spinach

½ cup grapefruit sections

1 small orange

4 medium strawberries

¾ cup raspberries

2 Tbsp chia seeds

2 cups water

Add all ingredients to the
NutriBullet Rx Short Cup and
extract until smooth.

SVELTE AND SWEET

SERVES:
2

2 cups spinach

½ cup cooked garbanzo beans

4 medium strawberries

4 mint leaves

1 banana

1 tsp cinnamon

2 cups unsweetened
almond milk

Add all ingredients to the
NutriBullet Rx Short Cup and
extract until smooth.

LEAN GREEN

¼ cup sliced cucumber

¼ cup sliced zucchini

2 small celery stalks

1 cup fresh pineapple

¾ cup baby kale

1 cup spinach

¼ cup fresh parsley

2 Tbsp chia seeds

2 tsp maca powder

2 cups coconut water

Add all ingredients to the **NutriBullet Rx Short Cup** and **extract** until smooth.

PEP STEP

SERVES: 2

2 cup collard greens
1 medium apple
  (cored)
1 cup fresh pineapple
½-inch sliced fresh ginger
1 Tbsp apple cider vinegar
  (raw)
2 tsp maca powder
2 cups coconut water

Add all ingredients to the
NutriBullet Rx Short Cup
and **extract** until smooth.

NICE AND SLOW

SERVES: 2

2 cups spinach
½ avocado
1 cup blackberries
½ cup rolled oats
2 tsp Ceylon cinnamon
2 cups unsweetened
  almond milk

Add all ingredients to the
NutriBullet Rx Short Cup and
extract until smooth.

SOUPER-
BLASTS

PEAR & CAULIFLOWER

SERVES:
4-6

½ head of cauliflower, chopped

1 pear, peeled and cored

1 Tbsp almond butter

1 Tbsp cold pressed virgin coconut oil

   OR extra virgin olive oil

1½ tbsp Dijon mustard

1 cup vegetable ***OR*** chicken broth *

1 cup plain, unsweetened almond milk

Salt and pepper to taste

* Cooled to room temperature for at least 30 minutes, if making it fresh!

Add all ingredients to the **SouperBlast Pitcher** and **extract** on the **7-Minute Heated Cycle.**

These delicious **SouperBlasts**—warm NutriBlasts made using the **NutriBullet Rx's 7-Minute Heated Cycle**—make for delicious meals any time of day. Ranging from light, detoxifying recipes to heartier mixtures, the **SouperBlasts** found in this section combine the best gifts the earth has to offer into one nourishing bowl.

COCONUT & RED PEPPER

SERVES:
4-6

2 large red bell peppers

2 Tbsp minced sweet onion or shallot

¼ garlic clove

2 ripe tomatoes, quartered

¼ cup organic coconut butter

1 cup water

1 cup light coconut milk

⅓ cup raw cashews, soaked 4-8 hours

⅛ tsp cayenne pepper

½ tsp turmeric

½ tsp Himalayan Salt

2 leaves fresh basil

Add all ingredients to the **SouperBlast Pitcher** and **extract** on the **7-Minute Heated Cycle.**

ZUCCHINI HEMP

SERVES:
4-6

3 zucchini,

 chopped into 1-inch cubes

4 small vine tomatoes

¾ cup fresh pineapple

¼ cup fresh parsley

1 Tbsp fresh dill, chopped

1 Tbsp apple cider vinegar

⅓ cup shelled raw hemp seeds

2 cups water

 OR vegetable broth *

Salt and pepper to taste

* Cooled to room temperature for at least 30 minutes, if making it fresh!

Add all ingredients to the **SouperBlast Pitcher** and **extract** on the **7-Minute Heated Cycle.**

GARDEN PARTY

4 Roma tomatoes, sliced into chunks

2 stalks celery, chopped

2 carrots, chopped

½ beet, chopped

¼ cup fresh chopped parsley

2 cups spinach

2 tsp hot sauce

Black pepper

2 cups vegetable broth *

* Cooled to room temperature for at least 30 minutes, if making it fresh!

Add all ingredients to the **SouperBlast Pitcher** and **extract** on the **7-Minute Heated Cycle.**

TOMATILLO GAZPACHO

SERVES:
4-6

1 Tbsp extra-virgin olive oil, divided

2 cloves garlic, roasted

1 English cucumber

1 avocado, peel removed and pitted

1 pound (*OR* 1-11oz can) tomatillos,
   husks removed

1 green bell pepper,
   seeds and stem removed

1-2 jalapeño peppers, seeded

¼ tsp salt

1 scallion

1 tsp raw honey *(optional)*

2 cups vegetable broth *

* Cooled to room temperature for at least 30 minutes, if making it fresh!

Add all ingredients to the **SouperBlast Pitcher** and **extract without heat.** Repeat rounds of extraction as needed to achieve desired consistency.

VEGGIE TORTILLA SOUP

SERVES:
6-8

1 can cooked Black beans, *

    plus an optional **½** can to add after

    extraction and before serving if a

    chunky consistency is desired

2 Tbsp canned green chili peppers

2 medium tomatoes,

    coarsely chopped

1 Tbsp olive oil

1 Tbsp chopped raw red onion

1 tsp cumin

½ tsp chili powder

2 red bell peppers

¼ tsp lime juice

2 cups vegetable broth *

*** Cooled to room temperature for at
least 30 minutes, if making it fresh!**

OPTIONAL GARNISHES

Cilantro

    (**2** tsp per bowl)

Sliced avocado

    (**2** slices per bowl)

Green onion

    (**2** tsp, chopped finely to

    garnish each bowl)

Roasted corn kernels

    (**1** Tbsp to garnish each bowl)

Add all ingredients, except for the optional
half can of black beans and garnishes, to
the **SouperBlast Pitcher** and **extract** on
the **7-Minute Heated Cycle**.

WHITE BEAN SOUP

2 cups cooked white beans *

(Cannellini or white Northern)

2 fresh sage leaves

1 Tbsp fresh rosemary

1 Tbsp extra virgin olive oil

2 cups vegetable stock *

¼ tsp salt

Black pepper to taste

* Cooled to room temperature for at least 30 minutes, if making it fresh!

Add all ingredients to the **SouperBlast Pitcher** and **extract** on the **7-Minute Heated Cycle.** Divide into serving dishes and enjoy!

DAVID WOLFE'S ROOT SOUP

SERVES:
4-6

4 small raw beets,
   rinsed and scrubbed

4 medium carrots,
   rinsed and scrubbed

1 cup chopped kale

2 stalks celery, trimmed

¼ cup fresh tarragon

1 tsp caraway seeds

½ tsp Himalayan salt

1 cup coconut water

1 cup water or vegetable broth *

fresh ground pepper to taste

* Cooled to room temperature for at least 30 minutes, if making it fresh!

Add all ingredients to the **SouperBlast Pitcher** and **extract** on the **7-Minute Heated Cycle.**

HEARTY SOUPS

HEARTY SOUPS

This section contains classic soup recipes. Filled with cooked vegetables and a wide variety of flavors and textures, their preparation is a bit more involved than that of their **SouperBlast** counterparts, but well worth the extra effort. From a satiating baked potato to a vegan clam chowder you'll swear is brimming with cream and shellfish, the recipes in this section are healthful, satisfying, and soupremely delicious!

RATATOUILLE SOUP

¼ cup olive oil

1 small yellow onion, diced

2 cloves minced garlic

½ large eggplant, diced with skin in tact

1 large red bell pepper, diced

1 large zucchini, diced

1 large yellow squash, diced

3 seeded and diced tomatoes

2 Tbsp chopped fresh basil

1½ cans (**OR** 3 cups cooked)*

    organic cannellini beans, rinsed
    and drained if canned

1 Tbsp tomato paste

2 cups vegetable **OR** chicken stock *

1 Tbsp lemon juice

½ tsp salt

Pepper to taste

1 Tbsp fresh chopped parsley, to garnish

* **Cooled to room temperature for at least 30 minutes, if making it fresh!**

1 Heat oil in a large soup pot over medium heat. Add onions and garlic and sauté until lightly browned, about 3 minutes. Add eggplant and thyme, stirring occasionally until the eggplant is partially cooked, about 3 minutes. Add the peppers, zucchini, and squash and cook for another 5 minutes. Stir in tomatoes, beans, tomato paste, vegetable stock, lemon juice, and salt and cover with a lid. Simmer for 5 minutes.

2 Remove the mixture from the heat and **allow to cool to room temperature, about 30 minutes to an hour.** To accelerate this process, transfer the pot to the refrigerator for 10-20 minutes.

3 Once cooled, add 2/3 of the mixture to the **SouperBlast Pitcher**. Transfer the remaining 1/3 to a microwave-safe dish or the stove top to reheat and stir in once the pureed soup has heated through.

"CLAM" CHOWDER

SERVES:
6-8

CASHEW BASE

1 cup cashews,

    soaked 3-12 hours

4 tsp arrowroot flour

2 cups vegetable

    OR chicken broth *

1½ tsp Worcestershire sauce

POT INGREDIENTS

1 Tbsp coconut oil

1 large yellow onion, diced

3 carrots

    peeled and chopped

3 stalks of celery,

    peeled and chopped

1½ cups (4 oz) shiitake mushrooms, sliced

2 cups (8 oz) white mushrooms, sliced

7 small red potatoes,

    scrubbed and quartered

2 sheets of nori, finely chopped

1 tsp salt

4 cups vegetable *OR* chicken broth *

2 Tbsp tomato paste

2 Tbsp lemon juice

* Cooled to room temperature for at least 30 minutes, if making it fresh!

1 Prepare the cashew base by draining the soaked cashews and adding them to the **SouperBlast Pitcher.** Add the arrowroot flour, broth, and Worcestershire sauce and **extract** until smooth, about 90 seconds.

2 In a large pot, heat coconut oil over medium heat. Add onions and carrots and cook until tender, about 5 minutes. Add mushrooms and celery and cook until the mushrooms are cooked through, but firm, to mimic the texture of clams. Add the chopped new potatoes, nori, salt, and remaining vegetable/chicken broth and cover to bring to a boil, then reduce to simmer over low heat for 10-15 minutes until potatoes are cooked through.

3 Slowly add the cashew cream base into the pot and simmer 5-8 minutes, stirring occasionally until desired thickness is achieved. Finally, stir in tomato paste and lemon juice, stir until fully combined, then remove from heat and serve.

"CREAM" OF MUSHROOM

1 cup sweet onion, diced

3 cloves garlic, minced

1 Tbsp fresh thyme

1 Tbsp fresh sage

16 oz button mushrooms

½ cup raw cashews

1 cup vegetable stock *,

　　plus **2** Tbsp. for water sauté

1 cup almond milk

1 tsp salt

Freshly ground black pepper to taste

Chopped fresh parsley and paprika to garnish

* **Cooled to room temperature for at least 30 minutes, if making it fresh!**

1 Add onions and two tbsp. vegetable stock to a pot over medium-high heat. Cook the onions in the liquid until translucent, about 5 minutes, stirring continuously and adding small amounts of vegetable stock as necessary to prevent sticking.

2 Add the minced garlic, thyme, and sage, and cook for an additional 2 minutes. Add sliced mushrooms and cook for 5 more minutes, stirring continuously until cooked through.

3 **Allow the pot mixture to cool to room temperature, at least 30 minutes.** You can accelerate this process by transferring to the refrigerator for 10-20 minutes.

4 Empty 2/3 of the pot's ingredients to the **SouperBlast Pitcher.** Add cashews, almond milk, and vegetable stock and **extract** on the 7-minute heated cycle until smooth and warm.

5 While the soup extracts reheat the remaining mushroom/onion mixture over medium heat, adding liquid if necessary.

6 Pour the extracted soup into bowls and top with a scoop of the solid mushroom mixture.

"CREAM" OF BROCCOLI

⅓ cup sweet onion, chopped *

1 small baking potato baked *

2 bunches broccoli florets, steamed *

2 cups plain, unsweetened almond milk

½ tsp Himalayan salt

Fresh ground pepper to taste

* **Cooled to room temperature for at least 30 minutes, if making it fresh!**

1 Steam broccoli and onion for about 5 min. Cook the potato either by baking, steaming, or roasting. Remove the skin.

2 **Allow all ingredients to cool fully.** Once cool, add all ingredients to the **SouperBlast Pitcher** and **extract** on the **7-Minute Heated Cycle**.

ROASTED PARSNIP & CAULIFLOWER

1 Tbsp olive oil

2 small shallots, diced

½ leek,
> white and light green part only,
> halved lengthwise, cleaned, and
> chopped coarse salt

3 small parsnips,
> peeled, quartered, cored, and diced

1 head cauliflower, roughly chopped

2½ cups water, chicken stock,
> **OR** vegetable stock *

1 bay leaf

1 Tbsp fresh chopped thyme leaves

2½ Tbsp fresh chopped tarragon leaves

2 Tbsp fresh chopped parsley

salt and pepper to taste

* **Cooled to room temperature for at least 30 minutes, if making it fresh!**

1 Heat the olive oil in a large heavy-bottomed soup pot over medium heat. Add the shallots, leek, and a pinch of salt and sauté, stirring until translucent and tender—about 5 minutes. Add the parsnips and cauliflower, and another pinch of salt. Partially cover the pot and cook for another 5-10 minutes, removing the lid periodically to stir the vegetables. When parsnips and cauliflower are cooked through but still firm, add the stock, bay leaf, thyme, tarragon, and parsley. Bring to a boil, then reduce to a simmer for 45 minutes, or until the vegetables are very soft and the soup is fragrant.

2 Remove the soup from the heat, remove the bay leaf, and transfer to the refrigerator until it has cooled completely — about 3 hours. Once cool, add all ingredients to the **SouperBlast Pitcher** and **extract** on the **7-minute Heated Cycle**.

PUMPKIN BEET

2 small beet root

1 cup pumpkin puree

   (*OR* may use **1** lb fresh pumpkin)

3-4 small new potatoes

2 tsp extra virgin olive oil

¼ cup onion, sliced

½ tsp cinnamon

¼ tsp nutmeg powder

¼ tsp salt

½ cup light coconut milk

1½ cups vegetable broth *

   (*OR* water)

2 Tbsp pumpkin seeds

   (for garnish)

Black pepper to taste

*** Cooled to room temperature for at
   least 30 minutes, if making it fresh!**

1 Preheat oven to 400 degrees F. Wash beets and potatoes well. Cut beets, potatoes, and pumpkin if using fresh into 1-2 inch pieces. Place on a baking tray along with sliced onion and lightly drizzle with olive oil and a light dusting of salt. Toss to coat. Bake for about 35-45 minutes until fork tender.

2 **Allow to cool for about 15-20 minutes.** You may place ingredients in the refrigerator to speed up the process. Place all ingredients (except pumpkin seeds) in the **SouperBlast Pitcher** and allow to run on the **7-minute Heating Cycle**.

3 Divide into serving bowls and top with some pumpkin seeds. Enjoy!

CHEESY BAKED POTATO SOUP
WITH TEMPEH BACON BITS

SERVES:
4-6

SOUP

2-3 Tbsp Nutritional Yeast

½ cup soaked and drained cashews

2 medium baking potatoes,

    cooked, skin removed *

1 cup plain unsweetened almond milk

1 cup vegetable broth *

½ Tbsp Dijon mustard

2 cloves roasted garlic *

½ tsp onion powder

salt and pepper to taste

diced chives to garnish *(optional)*

*** Cooled to room temperature for at
least 30 minutes, if making it fresh!**

1 Soak cashews in filtered water
overnight or for at least 4 hours;
drain liquid.

2 Cook potato either by baking it in the
oven at 350ºF for about 45 minutes
until fork tender or by peeling, cutting
into cubes and steaming in a steamer
basket. **Allow potato to cool** and
remove skin.

3 Roast garlic by peeling the outer papery
layer away from an entire head, cutting
the top end of the head to expose the
tips of all cloves, and roasting at 400
degrees for 30-35 minutes; you can also
purchase pre-roasted garlic cloves.

4 Combine all ingredients in the
SouperBlast Pitcher, top with the
Vent Top Lid and set to the **7-Minute
heating mode.** Divide among serving
bowls and top with optional tempeh
bacon bits!

TEMPEH BACON

1 package (8 ounces) tempeh

   cut into thin strips

   (to mimic the shape of bacon)

¼ cup soy sauce

¼ - ½ tsp liquid smoke

2 Tbsp maple syrup

1 Tbsp apple cider vinegar

---

1 In medium bowl, mix together the soy sauce, liquid smoke, vinegar, and maple syrup. Marinate sliced tempeh in the liquid mixture for at least 4 hours.

2 When ready to prepare, preheat oven to 325°F. Remove tempeh slices from liquid, pat excess liquid away with a clean towel, and place on a baking sheet lined with parchment paper. Bake for 20-25 minutes, flipping the pieces over half way through cooking time. Allow to cool slightly before chop into small bacon-bit sized pieces (if desired for soup). Refrigerate leftovers in a tightly sealed container for up to 4 days.

NUT
BUTTERS

There's something so comforting about the silky, savory-sweet taste of nut butter. From Classic Peanut to exotic Tropical Spice macadamia, the recipes in this section provide ideas to quickly and easily extract your own decadent concoctions for a fraction of the cost of retail varieties. Consult our list below, or experiment to create your own mixtures using 3 cups of nuts, ¼ cup of liquid, and ½ teaspoon of salt. Happy spreading!

CLASSIC OLD-FASHIONED PEANUT BUTTER

SERVES:

8 *2-TBSP SERVINGS*

3 cups roasted peanuts,
shells removed

¼ cup peanut
OR grapeseed oil

½ tsp sea salt

Add all ingredients to the **NutriBullet Rx Short Cup** and **extract** for **30 seconds**. Carefully remove the blade and stir ingredients to make sure the nuts reach the blade evenly. Repeat until the nuts form a smooth, even texture. This will take 3-6 rounds of extracting, removing the blade, and stirring.

HONEY ROASTED PEANUT

SERVES:
8 *2-TBSP SERVINGS*

This delicious recipe works best with home-roasted peanuts, as packaged honey roasted peanuts tend to be too dry to form a cohesive nut butter texture. Try atop apples for a sweet, yet healthful treat!

3 cups raw peanuts, shells removed

¼ cup honey

¼ tsp kosher salt

1 Preheat oven to 325 degrees Fahrenheit. Line a baking sheet with parchment paper.

2 In a large bowl, heat the honey in the microwave for 15-20 seconds until it reaches a liquid consistency. Add the peanuts and stir to coat.

3 Pour the honey-coated peanuts over the parchment-lined baking sheet in a flat layer. Roast for a total of 25 minutes, removing the sheet from the oven and turning the nuts over every five minutes to ensure an even roast.

4 Remove roasted peanuts from the oven and **allow to cool to room temperature, at least 30 minutes.** You can accelerate this process by transferring to the refrigerator for 10-20 minutes.

5 Once cool, add all ingredients to the **NutriBullet Rx Short Cup** and **extract** for **30 seconds**. Carefully remove the blade and stir ingredients to make sure the nuts reach the blade evenly. Repeat until the nuts form a smooth, even texture. This will take 3-6 rounds of extracting, removing the blade, and stirring.

PEANUT & COCONUT

SERVES:
8 2-TBSP
SERVINGS

---

3 cups roasted peanuts, shells removed

½ tsp sea salt

3 Tbsp maple syrup,

    agave nectar, blackstrap molasses, raw

    honey, or brown rice syrup *(optional)*

½ cup coconut butter

Add all ingredients to the **NutriBullet Rx Short Cup** and **extract** for **30 seconds**. Carefully remove the blade and stir ingredients to make sure the nuts reach the blade evenly. Repeat until the nuts form a smooth, even texture. This will take 3-6 rounds of extracting, removing the blade, and stirring.

ALMOND

3 cups raw or roasted almonds

½ tsp sea salt *(optional)*

¼ cup grapeseed,
     almond, or walnut oil

Add all ingredients to the **NutriBullet Rx Short Cup** and **extract** for **30 seconds**. Carefully remove the blade and stir ingredients to make sure the nuts reach the blade evenly. Repeat until the nuts form a smooth, even texture. This will take 3-6 rounds of extracting, removing the blade, and stirring.

CASHEW

3 cups raw or roasted cashews

½ tsp sea salt *(optional)*

¼ cup grapeseed,
     almond, or walnut oil

Add all ingredients to the **NutriBullet Rx Short Cup** and **extract** for **30 seconds**. Carefully remove the blade and stir ingredients to make sure the nuts reach the blade evenly. Repeat until the nuts form a smooth, even texture. This will take 3-6 rounds of extracting, removing the blade, and stirring.

COCONUT BUTTER

SERVES:
8 *2-TBSP SERVINGS*

3 cups unsweetened dry coconut flakes

2 Tbsp Virgin cold-pressed coconut oil

1 tsp pure vanilla extract *(optional)*

½ tsp Himalayan sea salt *(optional)*

Add all ingredients to the **NutriBullet Rx Short Cup** and **extract** for **30 seconds**. Carefully remove the blade and stir ingredients to make sure the nuts reach the blade evenly. Repeat until the nuts form a smooth, even texture. This will take 3-6 rounds of extracting, removing the blade, and stirring.

CHOCOLATE PECAN BUTTER

SERVES:
8 *2-TBSP SERVINGS*

3 cups toasted, unsalted pecans

3 heaping Tbsp. raw cacao powder

¼ cup raw honey

½ tsp sea salt

Add all ingredients to the **NutriBullet Rx Short Cup** and **extract** for **30 seconds**. Carefully remove the blade and stir ingredients to make sure the nuts reach the blade evenly. Repeat until the nuts form a smooth, even texture. This will take 3-6 rounds of extracting, removing the blade, and stirring.

NOT-ELLA

SERVES:
8 *2-TBSP SERVINGS*

3 cup toasted unsalted hazelnuts

¼ cup maple syrup,

   raw honey, or agave nectar

3 Tbsp raw cacao powder

1-2 Tbsp filtered water

1 tsp coconut oil

1 tsp pure vanilla extract

¼ - ½ tsp Himalayan Sea Salt

1 Remove hazelnut skins by rolling the nuts in a slightly damp tea towel.

2 Add all ingredients to the **NutriBullet Rx Short Cup** and **extract** for **30 seconds**. Carefully remove the blade and stir ingredients to make sure the nuts reach the blade evenly. Repeat until the nuts form a smooth, even texture. This will take 3-6 rounds of extracting, removing the blade, and stirring.

MAPLE CINNAMON WALNUT

SERVES:

8 *2-TBSP SERVINGS*

3 cups dry roasted walnuts

¼ cup maple syrup

2 tsp cinnamon

½ tsp sea salt

Add all ingredients to the **NutriBullet Rx Short Cup** and **extract** for **30 seconds**. Carefully remove the blade and stir ingredients to make sure the nuts reach the blade evenly. Repeat until the nuts form a smooth, even texture. This will take 3-6 rounds of extracting, removing the blade, and stirring.

TROPICAL SPICE BUTTER

SERVES:

8 *2-TBSP SERVINGS*

1 cup raw, unsalted cashews

1 cup raw, unsalted macadamia nuts

½ cup unsweetened shredded coconut

¼ tsp turmeric

¼ tsp ginger

½ tsp Ceylon cinnamon

¼ cup tbsp raw honey,

    maple syrup, or agave nectar *(optional)*

Add all ingredients to the **NutriBullet Rx Short Cup** and **extract** for **30 seconds**. Carefully remove the blade and stir ingredients to make sure the nuts reach the blade evenly. Repeat until the nuts form a smooth, even texture. This will take 3-6 rounds of extracting, removing the blade, and stirring.

SUPERFOOD ELIXIRS

COLD BREWS & HOT DRINKS

The following beverages taste like desserts and calorie-laden coffee drinks, but are actually loaded with delicious, highly nutritious superfoods! Using high-quality ingredients like **cacao**, **goji berries**, **maca**, and **raw honey**, these beverages satisfy even the most extreme sweet tooth without leading you off track from your healthy lifestyle.

ALMOND COFFEE COOLER

1 cup brewed coffee *

1 Tbsp almond butter

1 cup unsweetened almond milk

1 Tbsp raw honey

½ tsp nutmeg

1 cup crushed ice

Dash of cinnamon

* **Cooled to room temperature for at least 30 minutes, if making it fresh!**

Place all ingredients into the **NutriBullet Rx Short Cup** and **extract** for 25 seconds.

PEANUT BUTTER CUP

1 cup brewed coffee *

¼ cup dairy-free creamer
(coconut milk or organic
soy milk)

¼ cup peanut butter

2 Tbsp raw cacao powder *OR* nibs

1 tsp vanilla extract

1 cup ice cubes

*** Cooled to room temperature
for at least 30 minutes, if
making it fresh!**

Place all ingredients into the
NutriBullet Rx Short Cup and
extract for 25 seconds.

CARAMEL COOLER

1 cup brewed coffee *

2 pitted dates

1 tsp Coconut oil

1 Tbsp cashew butter

1 tsp Maple syrup

¼ tsp vanilla extract

Dash of salt

½ cup almond milk

½ cup ice cubes

*** Cooled to room temperature
for at least 30 minutes, if
making it fresh!**

Place all ingredients into the
NutriBullet Rx Short Cup and
extract for 25 seconds.

COCONUT MOCHA DELIGHT

1 cup freshly brewed coffee *

1 cup coconut water

1 tsp reishi mushroom powder

½ tsp maca powder

1-3 drops vanilla liquid Stevia

1 Tbsp cold-pressed coconut oil

* Cooled to room temperature for at least 30 minutes, if making it fresh!

Place all ingredients into the **SouperBlast Pitcher** and **extract** on the **7-minute Heated Cycle.**

SWEET CINNAMON CHAI

1 cup chai tea, brewed *

2 pitted dates

¼ tsp Ceylon cinnamon

½ cup hazelnut milk

   (may use almond milk)

½ ripe banana *(optional)*

* Cooled to room temperature for at least 30 minutes, if making it fresh!

Place all ingredients into the **SouperBlast Pitcher** and **extract** on the **7-minute Heated Cycle.**

DAIRY-FREE HOT CHOCOLATE

1½ cups light coconut milk

(from a can)

2 Tbsp raw cacao powder

2 tsp cold-pressed coconut oil

1 Tbsp raw honey

½ tsp pure vanilla extract

Place all ingredients into the **SouperBlast Pitcher** and **extract** on the **7-minute Heated Cycle.**

HOT CINNAMON APPLE CIDER

1 apple

(core and seeds removed)

½ tsp cinnamon

1 cup water

½ cup pure apple juice

1 Tbsp apple cider vinegar

1 clove *(optional)*

Place all ingredients into the **SouperBlast Pitcher** and **extract** on the **7-minute Heated Cycle.**

SUPERFOOD SUPERBOOST HOT TODDIE

12 oz filtered water

2 Tbsp SuperFood SuperBoost

2 tsp cold-pressed coconut oil

2 tsp raw honey

Place all ingredients into the **SouperBlast Pitcher** and **extract** on the **7-minute Heated Cycle.**

GOJI BERRY LIGHT ROAST

1 cup brewed light roast coffee *

3 Tbsp dried goji berries

1 cup water

1 tsp maca powder

* Cooled to room temperature for at least 30 minutes, if making it fresh!

Place all ingredients into the **SouperBlast Pitcher** and **extract** on the **7-minute Heated Cycle.**

PUMPKIN SPICE LATTE

1 shot espresso * (*OR* ½ cup strong brewed coffee)

1½ cups vanilla almond milk (may also use organic vanilla soy or hazelnut milk)

1 Tbsp canned pure pumpkin puree

½ tsp pumpkin pie spice (may sub cinnamon and nutmeg)

¼ tsp vanilla extract

5 drops vanilla liquid Stevia (may use 1-2 tsp raw honey) (*optional*)

* Cooled to room temperature for at least 30 minutes, if making it fresh!

Place all ingredients into the **SouperBlast Pitcher** and **extract** on the **7-minute Heated Cycle.**

PEPPERMINT MOCHA

2-3 fresh mint leaves

1 cup fresh brewed coffee *

1 Tbsp cacao powder

1 cup unsweetened almond milk

2 drops peppermint extract (*optional* for a more minty punch)

* Cooled to room temperature for at least 30 minutes, if making it fresh!

Place all ingredients into the **SouperBlast Pitcher** and **extract** on the **7-minute Heated Cycle.**

SUPERFOODS

GO TO WWW.NUTRILIVING.COM TO ORDER

SUPERCHARGE

SUPERCHARGE YOUR NUTRIBLASTS!

AT NUTRIBULLET, WE PRIDE OURSELVES ON SHARING THE MOST UP-TO-DATE KNOWLEDGE ABOUT NUTRITION AND WELLNESS WITH ALL OF OUR USERS. From exalting the benefits of extracted nutrition to providing the most current research regarding the impact of fruits and vegetables on health, our primary goal is to empower you with the skills you need to optimize your health.

This is why we've created our own line of SuperFood SuperBoosts to add to your Nutri-Blasts, **NutriBlast Rx's,** and **SouperBlasts**! These formulas contain some of the world's most powerful superfoods in easy-to-use powdered form.

- SuperFood Protein Blend
- SuperFood Fat Burning Boost
- SuperFood Beauty Boost
- SuperFood SuperBoost
- SuperFood Healthy Gut
- SuperFood Spice Blend
- SuperFood Cleansing Greens
- SuperFood SuperKids

Whether you're looking to lose weight, boost your energy, maximize your intake of antioxidants, or simply incorporate a greater variety of plant foods into your daily diet, these mixtures contain the fuel you need to SuperBoost your wellness goals!

TAKE QUIZ TODAY!

THE PERSONALIZED PRESCRIPTION

WWW.NUTRILIVING.COM

WOMEN ONLY

27 HOW OFTEN DO YOU EXPERIENCE HOT FLASHES OR NIGHT SWEATS?

- Never
- Seldom
- Sometimes
- Often
- Everyday

RED   ORANGE YELLOW GREEN   **BLUE**

28 DO YOU EXPERI... MENSTRUAL CY...

- No
- Yes

MEN ONLY

HOW OFTEN DO YOU GET SUGAR CRAVINGS?

RED   ORANGE YELLOW GREEN   **BLUE**

5	
10	
15	
20	

THE QUIZ

01 WHAT IS YOUR SEX?

- Male
- Female

RED   ORANGE

LIVE THE NUTRI-LIFESTYLE ON NUTRILIVING.COM

NUTRILIVING.COM IS A COMMUNITY FOR NU-TRIBULLET OWNERS CENTERED ENTIRELY AROUND YOUR PERSONAL HEALTH NEEDS. Not everyone is the same, after all, and not everyone should get the same advice for healthy living. That's why we've gathered experts on nutrition—Registered Dietitians, Nutritionists, trained community moderators and more—to provide you with the information you can't find anywhere else, all in one place.

We're here to help you learn all you can about your health. From fibromyalgia recovery information to weight loss advice and more, the content featured on this site will help you grow healthier, happier, and more vibrant, all with your NUTRIBULLET in hand!

> It's the support you need right at your fingertips. All you need to get started is your **NutriBullet Rx** serial number.

We've got articles, recipes, video information on healing foods, and even a forum and profile page where you can interact with other Blasters and share your stories, experiences, questions and more.

Go to **Nutriliving.com** today and join the fun!

INDEX

NUTRIBLAST
Rx's

NUT
BUTTERS

SUPERFOOD
ELIXIRS